Dad set up the barbecue.

"Lots of smoke," said Chip.

"But not barbecue smoke!"
said Biff.

It was a hut on fire!

"Get the firefighters,"
said Chip.

The fire engine came.

"Get back," said the firefighter.

"It's hot," said Biff.

"It's a big fire," said Chip.

The firefighters put the
fire out.

"Lots of smoke," said Mum.

"Lots of barbecue smoke!"
said Kipper.

They ran back.

"Oh no," said Mum.

"The barbecue!" said Dad.

"Get the firefighters!"
said Biff.